UNIT 18

ISBN 978-1-60218-557-9
ISBN 1-60218-557-3
167311

12 11 10 09 08   2 3 4 5 6

 Sopris West®
EDUCATIONAL SERVICES

A Cambium Learning® Company

BOSTON, MA · LONGMONT, CO

UNIT 18
The Reef

The Great Barrier Reef

by Ann Watanabe

Look at the picture. It shows a bird's-eye view of the Great Barrier Reef. What is a bird's-eye view? What do you see? Across thousands of years, the Great Barrier Reef has been built by tiny animals. What questions do you have about the Great Barrier Reef?

Chapters 1, 2

Vocabulary

★ **Aus·tra·lia**

Australia is one of Earth's seven continents. The continent has one country, and the country is also called Australia.

For our vacation, we sailed south to *Australia*. What continent did we visit? What country did we visit?

Australia

★ **cor·al reef**

A **coral reef** is an underwater habitat built by small animals called coral polyps.

John swam underwater and saw a *coral reef*. Many animals were living in and around the . . .

★ **e·co·sys·tem**

An **ecosystem** is a community of animals and plants living together in one area.

A pond and all the plants and animals in and around it are called an *ecosystem*. A rain forest is another . . .

★ = New

★ **ap·prox·i·mate·ly**

If you do not know the exact number of something, but you can make a good guess, you say **"approximately."**

About and *around* often mean *approximately.* How many students are in our class? Don't count. Just use the word approximately.

Now You Try It!

Try defining the next word. Then look up the word in the glossary. Your definition might be better!

con·ti·nent

Start with "A *continent* is . . ."
Let's find the word on page 69.

Chapter 1

The Blue Planet

From Space

    Close your eyes and imagine yourself in space. Now open your eyes and look down on Earth—the blue planet. Earth looks blue from space because there is so much water covering its surface.

Why is Earth called the blue planet?

Look for the Pacific Ocean in the photo. Now find the continent of Australia.

Find the Great Barrier Reef of Australia. The Great Barrier Reef is made up of thousands of coral reefs and hundreds of islands. It is so large that you can see it from space. Unlike a continent, the coral reefs are alive.

Touch the Great Barrier Reef. Describe what it's made up of.

Rich With Life

The Great Barrier Reef stretches across 1,240 miles. Except for the rain forests, coral reefs have more types of animals than any other ecosystem. The Great Barrier Reef is home to:

About 1,500 types of fish

Seahorses   Clownfish

Around 5,000 types of mollusks

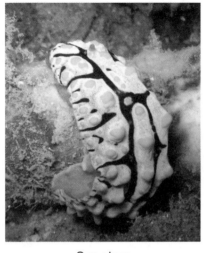

Sea slugs

Giant clams

Approximately 360 types of hard coral

Staghorn coral

Plate coral

Describe the different types of animals you might see at the Great Barrier Reef.

FACT

1. What is the Great Barrier Reef?

DESCRIPTION

2. Describe the different types of animals you might see at the Great Barrier Reef.

INFERENCE

3. Why do you think scientists use the words "about," "around," and "approximately" to tell how many types of animals are found at the Great Barrier Reef?

PERSONAL RESPONSE

4. Would you like to visit the Great Barrier Reef? Why or why not?

Chapter 2

Food Chains in the Reef

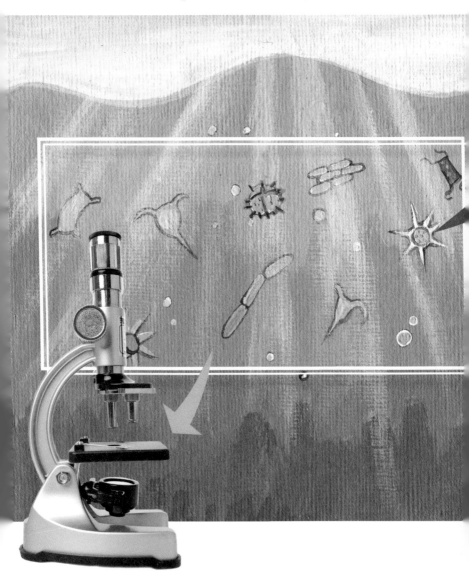

Sunlight shines through the water. Tiny little plants called phytoplankton soak up the sun's rays.

A hungry shrimp feeds on the phytoplankton.

A longnose hawkfish swoops down from its perch on top of a sea fan. It snatches the shrimp for a tasty meal.

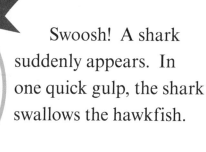

Swoosh! A shark suddenly appears. In one quick gulp, the shark swallows the hawkfish.

oint to each picture and describe the food chain.

Like all ecosystems, coral reefs have many food chains. At the beginning of these food chains are plants that make their own food from the sun. Next on the chain are the plant eaters—the herbivores. Finally, there are the meat eaters—the carnivores—and those that eat both meat and plants—the omnivores.

Carnivores

Herbivores

Plant-like Algae

What does an omnivore eat?

Herbivores, Carnivores, and Omnivores on the Reef

Can you tell what each animal is—herbivore, carnivore, or omnivore?

When I'm an adult, I feed on seaweed and seagrass. Isn't that sweet? What am I—an herbivore, carnivore, or omnivore?

Green Sea Turtle

Dwarf Minke Whale

I eat fish and tiny animals called krill. Such delicious treats! What am I—an herbivore, carnivore, or omnivore?

I can puff myself up so other fish won't eat me. I eat seaweed, coral, and small animals that live on the ocean floor. What am I —an herbivore, carnivore, or omnivore?

Starry Pufferfish

The Reef Community

Who are we? We are members of the Great
Barrier Reef community. We depend on each other.

19

Miss Tam at the Great Barrier Reef

by Marilyn Sprick and Paula Rich
illustrated by Page Eastburn O'Rourke

Miss Tam is a retired librarian from Montgomery, Alabama. This is her third grand travel adventure. Can you tell where Miss Tam has put the bright pink hatpin?

Chapters 1, 2

Vocabulary

★ **in·flat·able**

Something **inflatable** can be filled with air or water.

We pumped up our *inflatable* raft and floated down the river. Name three inflatable things.

★ **reg·u·la·tor**

When you scuba dive, you put a **regulator** in your mouth to breathe. It is connected to an air tank.

Before John jumped off the boat to go diving, he put a tank on his back and a *regulator* in his mouth. He needed the regulator so he could . . .

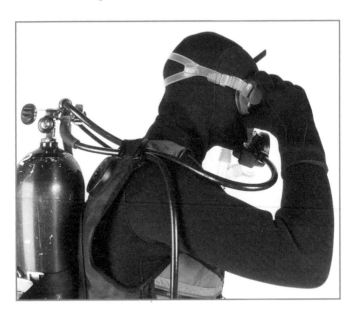

★ = New

★ lei·sure·ly

When you do something in a **leisurely** way, you take your time.

Aunt Sue took a *leisurely* walk through the garden. She stopped often and smelled the flowers. When you take your time eating, you eat . . .

Now You Try It!

Try defining the next word. Then look up the word in the glossary. Your definition might be better!

★ re·view

Start with "*Review* means to . . ."
Let's find the word on page 72.

★ = New

Chapter 1

Suiting Up

Miss Tam sat in a big boat off the coast of Australia. Water glistened in every direction.

Miss Tam was very excited. Today would be her first dive. She couldn't wait to see the giant clams, clownfish, eels, and, of course, pufferfish and octopuses. Miss Tam smiled. "Here I come—Miss Tam to the Great Barrier Reef."

The dive instructor handed Miss Tam a black rubbery suit. "Oh my," said Miss Tam as she looked at the suit. It seemed a bit small. Nonetheless, she stuck her feet through the leg holes and tried to pull the suit up her legs. It wouldn't budge!

Where is Miss Tam? What is she going to do?

"Oh my," thought Miss Tam. Determined, she stood up and tugged again. The suit came up to her knees and stopped. Miss Tam sighed and looked around. Right–left, right–left, people were dancing from foot to foot as they wiggled into their wetsuits. Miss Tam thought the dance was worth a try.

Right, tug, left, tug. Finally, the tight black suit was up as far as her waist. "Phew!" said Miss Tam.

The instructor smiled at Miss Tam. "Good on ya, mate! You're halfway there," he said. In her best Aussie English, Miss Tam mumbled, "Ah, good on us."

Why were people dancing from foot to foot? Why did Miss Tam's instructor say, "Good on ya, mate"?

Miss Tam watched as others on the boat began a second dance. Left–right, left–right . . . Miss Tam leaned over and pushed her left hand down its sleeve, then right–left–right, until, finally, her hands reached air. "Phew!" said Miss Tam as she wiggled and bent her fingers to make sure she could still feel them.

Just as she thought she was ready—zip! Her instructor closed up the back of her wetsuit. "Oh my," thought Miss Tam, but she couldn't say a thing. The suit was so tight she felt like a stuffed sausage.

Why did Miss Tam feel like a stuffed sausage?

But there was more! Miss Tam had to strap a 10-pound weight belt around her waist. Then the instructor helped her into an inflatable vest that held a 30-pound tank of air. Next, they sorted through the tangle of hoses so everything was in its right position. Finally, the instructor went through the safety check and reviewed the dive instructions.

With the safety check done, Miss Tam sat down heavily on a wooden bench. She carefully put her face mask over her eyes and nose so it wouldn't leak. She was ready. "Great Barrier Reef, here I come," she thought.

SETTING

1. Where does the story take place?

GOAL

2. Why did Miss Tam go to the Great Barrier Reef?

PREDICTION

3. What do you think Miss Tam will see?

PERSONAL RESPONSE

4. How would you feel if you were Miss Tam? Why?

Chapter 2

Jumping In

Suddenly, the dive instructor bellowed, "Time to get wet!"

Miss Tam waddled like a penguin toward the gate on the side of the boat. She held onto the side of the boat as she tugged on one big pink fin at a time. She stood at the gate, put her regulator in her mouth, and took a deep breath.

The instructor was waiting in the clear blue water. He motioned to Miss Tam. Miss Tam put one bright pink foot forward. "Oh my," she said. Through her regulator it sounded more like "Mmm mmm." Then Miss Tam jumped feet-first into the deep blue ocean.

Once she was in the water, Miss Tam's inflatable vest kept her bobbing on the surface while she breathed rapidly through her regulator. The instructor motioned for her to let the air out of her vest. Within seconds, Miss Tam and her instructor were sinking into the ocean. Nervous but excited, Miss Tam thought, "Parrotfish, giant clams . . . Great Barrier Reef, here I come!"

Surrounded by water, Miss Tam gradually relaxed. With a flip of her fin, she glided through the ocean water. Miss Tam thought, "I feel like a fish." A six-foot moray eel swam by. Miss Tam thought, "Well, I'll be." Then she remembered her best Aussie English and tried to say "hooly-dooly" to her dive instructor. Through the regulator, it came out "oody-oody!"

On the boat, Miss Tam felt like a penguin. Why? Now that she's in the water, Miss Tam feels like a fish. Why?

Miss Tam's dive instructor carefully guided her around the reef. The coral was so colorful! Miss Tam was amazed. She wanted to reach out and touch the waving sea fans, the funny fat pufferfish, and the huge plates of coral, but she was very careful not to touch anything. Striped angelfish swam nearby, little orange and white clownfish looked up at her from the sea anemones, and a huge twelve-foot manta ray swept past above her.

escribe what Miss Tam saw on her dive.

That evening, Miss Tam sat in her hotel room. After finishing a luscious lemon rice pudding with pears and vanilla ice cream, she settled in for a leisurely rereading of a book about the Great Barrier Reef. Miss Tam opened the book. Colorful coral, graceful fish fluttering through the coral, a spotted eel staring right out of the page . . . Miss Tam thought, "Oh my. It is a wonder!" Then, before she knew it, she was snoring. It had been an eventful day on the Great Barrier Reef!

What did Miss Tam eat after her dive? Why was it an *eventful* day? Why do you think Miss Tam ordered rice pudding?

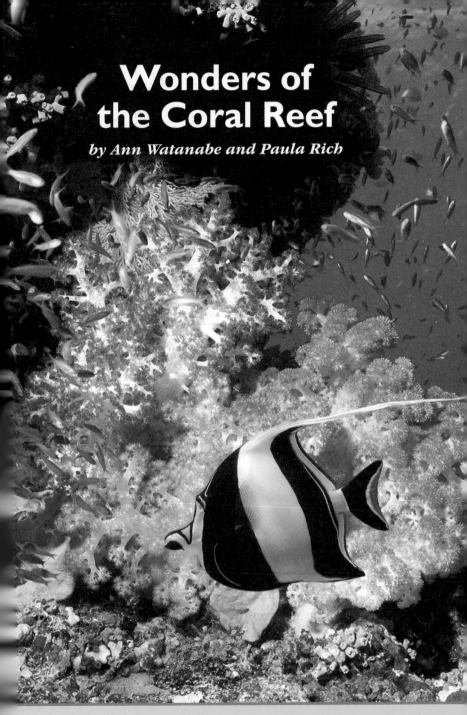

Wonders of the Coral Reef

by Ann Watanabe and Paula Rich

What do you already know about a coral reef? What questions do you have about a coral reef?

Chapters 1, 2

Vocabulary

★ cor·al pol·yp

A **coral polyp** is a sea animal with a tube-shaped body. Most are very small. Millions of coral polyps live together to form a coral reef.

Coral polyps live together to form coral reefs, and coral reefs are found in the ocean. So where will you find coral polyps?

★ al·gae

Algae are living things that are usually found in water. Some kinds of algae are too small to see, and others grow very large.

Seaweed that washes up on the beach is one kind of *algae*. The green scum you see floating on a pond is another kind of algae. Where else do you think you might find algae?

★ = New

★ nu·di·branch

A **nudibranch** (noo-duh-brank) is an animal that lives in the ocean. It has a soft body and is also called a sea slug.

Marisa had to write a report about *nudibranchs*, but she didn't know how to spell the word. What else could she call the animals in her report?

Now You Try It!

Try defining the next word. Then look up the word in the glossary. Your definition might be better!

col·o·ny

Start with "A *colony* is . . ."
Let's find the word on page 69.

Chapter 1

Reef Builders

Coral polyps are amazing little animals. Across thousands of years, coral polyps have built the Great Barrier Reef.

Coral Polyp

If you were a coral polyp on the Great Barrier Reef:

- You would live in a colony. Your small tube-shaped body, called a coral polyp, would be attached to the reef. You would also be attached to the other polyps in your colony.

- You would build a skeleton outside your body to protect yourself.

- You would be fussy about where you lived. You would need clean, clear ocean water—not too hot and not too cold.

- During the day, you would hide in your skeleton. At night, your tentacles would reach out to catch food. Stingers on your tentacles would help you catch your prey— tiny animals floating in the water.

Describe a coral polyp's habitat. Explain how a coral polyp gets food.

- If you were a coral polyp, tiny algae would grow inside of you—small plant-like things that make energy from the sun. The algae would make you look like you were a wonderful color—red, pink, purple, green, or yellow.

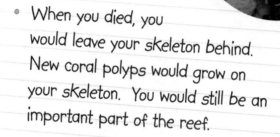

- When you died, you would leave your skeleton behind. New coral polyps would grow on your skeleton. You would still be an important part of the reef.

If you were a little coral polyp, you would be an amazing animal. You would be very important to the blue planet, but you wouldn't know it. Like your relative the jellyfish, you would have no brain!

FACT

1. What is a coral polyp?

DESCRIPTION

2. Describe a coral polyp.

EXPLANATION

3. Why does a coral polyp build a skeleton outside its body?

EXPLANATION

4. What gives a coral polyp its color?

PERSONAL RESPONSE

5. Would you like to be a coral polyp? Why or why not?

Chapter 2

What Would You Be?

If you could choose to be an animal on the Great Barrier Reef, what would you be? Among the many species, your choices would be almost endless. Would you want to be an important but brainless little coral polyp? An ancient sea turtle? How about a nudibranch? Or a shape-shifting octopus?

Nudibranch (noo-duh-brank)

If you were a nudibranch:

- People would call you a sea slug because your relatives are slugs. Like land slugs, you would have a soft body. Unlike land slugs, you would be colorful. You would be a dazzling little creature—a wonder of the sea.

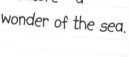

- You might *be* small—a half-inch or so—or you might *be* as long as two feet. You might look like a Spanish dancer with your skirts twirling or like a leafy green head of lettuce. What a strange little creature you would *be*.

- You would crawl slowly across the coral.

- You would enjoy eating sea anemones, seaweed, and sponges. You would be a predator.

- If a young fish decided to make a meal out of you, it would be a mistake. Nudibranchs taste awful. The fish would quickly spit you out!

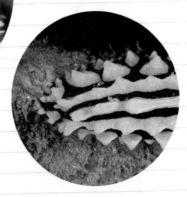

Octopus

If you were an octopus:

- You might live on the Great Barrier Reef. You would have eight incredible arms. Imagine having eight arms with many suckers to use for crawling.

- You would have no bones, so you could stretch out to twice your size. Or, you could squeeze up tight so you could slither through tiny cracks and into small spaces. Imagine what you could do.

- If a diver visited your home, you would play hide-and-seek. You would be hard to spot. You would change your color. You would be a master of disguise. You would make your skin look bumpy like the coral or smooth like a sponge.

- If someone got too close, you might even squirt a cloud of black ink and quickly swim away!

If you could choose to be an animal on the Great Barrier Reef, what would you be?

Pete the Pufferfish

by Jessica Sprick and Marilyn Sprick
illustrated by Ruth Galloway

Look at the picture. Describe what you see.

Chapters 1, 2

Vocabulary

★ dis·guise

Something that hides or changes the way you look is called a **disguise**.

Pam wanted to wear a *disguise*, so she put on a fake nose and glasses. What is another disguise you could wear?

★ ad·vi·sor

A person who gives advice is called an **advisor**.

At school, if you need an *advisor*, you can talk to a teacher, a counselor, or the principal. Who else can be an advisor?

Now You Try It!

Try defining the next word. Then look up the word in the glossary. Your definition might be better!

cor·al reef

Start with "A *coral reef* is . . ." Let's find the word on page 70.

★ = New

Chapter 1

Reef Community

Long, long ago on a busy ocean reef, there lived a little spotted pufferfish named Pete. Pete hatched from an egg on the ocean floor. Then he drifted in the big open ocean. Pete loved the peace and quiet of his ocean home.

But Pete, like other pufferfish, couldn't stay in the open ocean. It was far too dangerous. When he was big enough, he decided to make his way to the safety of the Great Barrier Reef.

Why did Pete need to make his way to the Great Barrier Reef?

Once at the big reef, Pete was amazed by all the commotion. Strange and wonderful animals zipped and swooshed in the water around him. Purple, blue, green, yellow . . . spotted, striped, and spiny fish zoomed past. Animals squeezed through cracks in the rocks and darted in and out of the coral. Then Pete saw a very strange sight. "That lettuce is walking!" he exclaimed.

escribe Pete's new home.

Just then Pete heard a giggle. The lettuce was giggling! "Ha! Fooled you," said the walking vegetable. "I'm Sasha the Sea Slug."

Pete laughed. Sasha had green leafy-looking growths on her body that looked like lettuce. Sasha had grown a disguise. The reef was much more interesting than Pete had ever dreamed.

Pete explored the wonders of the reef. He made friends. Calm Mother Octopus and wise Grandfather Sea Turtle became his advisors. The reef was an incredible community.

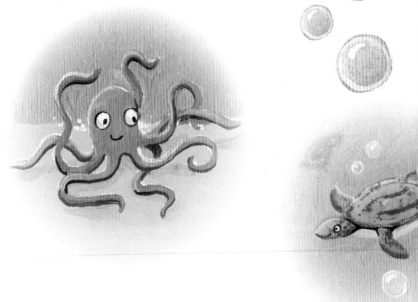

Why do you think Sasha looked like lettuce?
Who were Pete's advisors? What do advisors do?

Pete was amazed at how different all of the animals were. They all had special ways to survive in the ocean wilderness. The tiny little seahorse could change colors, the giant clam had a big thick shell, and the grumpy moray eel blended into the cracks of the rocks.

As Pete settled into his new life on the Great Barrier Reef, he decided to learn how to protect himself.

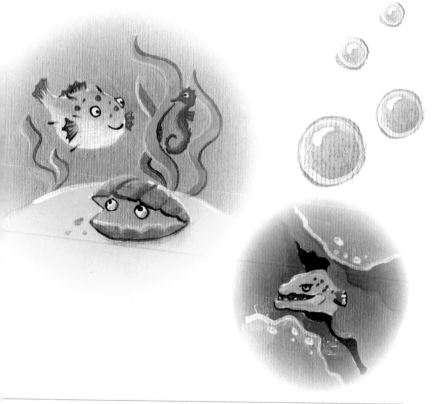

What did Pete need to learn to do?

SETTING

1. Where does the story take place?

MAIN CHARACTER, GOAL

2. Who is the main character, and what does he want?

DESCRIPTION

3. Describe Pete's friends.

PREDICTION

4. How do you think Mother Octopus and Grandfather Sea Turtle will help Pete?

Chapter 2

A Tight Squeeze

Pete swam over to see Mother Octopus and Grandfather Sea Turtle. He hoped they would have good advice. Pete said, "Mother Octopus and Grandfather Sea Turtle, there are many different animals on this reef, and it seems that every animal has a different way to protect itself. But I don't know how to stay safe from the fish that want to eat me. Can you help me?"

Mother Octopus crossed two of her long slender arms as she thought about Pete's question. Finally, she said, "I can teach you how to stay safe from hungry animals. Follow me."

Mother Octopus swam toward a small crack in the rocks below. She looked at Pete and said, "When danger is near, you must hide!" Then Mother Octopus said, "Think about changing your shape to fit where you want to go. Suck in your stomach and squeeze. Watch."

How is Mother Octopus trying to help Pete? What is her advice?

Mother Octopus disappeared into the tiny crack. Pete looked at Grandfather Sea Turtle. The ancient turtle shrugged his flippers. He wasn't so sure Pete could squeeze into the tiny crack. Pete had a bit of a round belly. Mother Octopus called from inside the crack, "Come on, Pete! You can do it!"

Pete thought and thought about changing his shape. His face turned blue. He sucked in his stomach so hard he could barely breathe. Then Pete squished himself as far as he could into the crack. "I DID IT! Mother Octopus, I did it!" Pete cried. But as soon as Pete spoke, his little stomach popped out. He was stuck.

Look at the pictures. Tell what's happening to Pete.

Chapters 3, 4

Vocabulary

★ con·tor·tion

When something is twisted out of its usual shape, it is called a **contortion**.

The magician went through many *contortions* to squeeze himself into a tiny box. If I put my arm behind my head like this, it is called a . . .

★ frus·trat·ed

If you are **frustrated**, you are upset and discouraged.

When things don't go the way you want them to, it's easy to get *frustrated*. What's another way to say "Isaac got upset and lost hope when his bike tire went flat"?

★ = New

★ con·fused

When you don't understand something, you are **confused**.

The road signs didn't match the map, and Mr. Chapman was *confused* about which way to go. Why was Mr. Chapman confused?

Chapter 3

Try This!

Poor Pete. He was stuck in a small crack in the rocks. He tried to wriggle out, but he was wedged so tightly that he couldn't move at all! "Uh, oh," said Pete. Grandfather Sea Turtle and Mother Octopus pushed on the rocks and tugged Pete's fins. Finally, he was free.

Pete rested on a piece of coral, rubbing his sore head and tail. "I am determined," Mother Octopus said. "Where there is a will, there is a way. Try this!" Then Mother Octopus squirted out a cloud of ink. From inside the black cloud, Mother Octopus said, "Ink will allow you to escape from a hungry predator. A big hungry fish can't see you through a cloud of black ink."

At that moment, Pete found himself lost in a sea of black. He couldn't see a thing. He swam blindly in a circle. "Ouch!" he yelled as he bumped into the reef.

Look at the pictures. Describe what's happening.

When the ink cleared, Grandfather Sea Turtle said, "Perhaps ink isn't the best idea for you either. We will just have to try something else." Then Grandfather Sea Turtle suggested they find a shell for Pete. "The big fish won't try to eat you if you have a shell."

Pete thought a shell was a great idea. They all swam around the reef looking for an empty shell that Pete could use. Some shells were too big; others were too small. Finally, they found a shell that was just right. Happily, Pete put the shell on his back, but it was so heavy that he sank to the ocean floor!

Nothing was working. Pete still didn't know how to protect himself.

Mother Octopus said, "Be back here at 6:00 a.m. I have another idea."

Look at the pictures. Tell what's happening.

Think and Talk

GOAL

1. What does Pete need to learn to do?

CHARACTERS

2. Who are Pete's advisors?

ACTION

3. What were Mother Octopus's suggestions? Did they work?

ACTION

4. What was Grandfather Sea Turtle's suggestion? Did it work?

Chapter 4

Pete's Trick

In the morning, Pete and Grandfather Sea Turtle met at the fire coral. Mother Octopus had summoned Lady Ann the Seahorse. Mother Octopus said, "Lady Ann came all the way from the seagrass to help. She can show Pete how to protect himself from the big fish!"

Without a word, Lady Ann swam to a patch of purple fire coral and disappeared. Pete was amazed. "I want to learn that trick!" said Pete.

Lady Ann gradually reappeared. "I know no tricks," said Lady Ann. "When I swim in front of something, I change colors to match it. Perhaps if you looked more like me, you could do this as well."

Pete gave it a try. He screwed up his nose, swam upright like the horse, and crooked his tail. Despite all his contortions, his color didn't change.

What was Lady Ann's suggestion? Did this work for Pete?

Imagining himself in the belly of a shark, Pete became quite distressed. Nothing was working. He was so frustrated that he gulped some water and let it out again with a sigh. Mother Octopus looked at Pete. "That's it!" she said. "You did it. You can protect yourself. Do it again."

Pete looked confused. "Do what?" he asked.

Grandfather Sea Turtle said, "Do what you did just before you sighed."

Pete still looked confused, but he sucked in a huge gulp of water.

"Look," said Mother Octopus. "Look! Your spines are sticking out, and you are big, fat, and round! No fish will try to eat you like that!" Pete was surprised to see that his spines were sticking out and his body had puffed up like a balloon. Pete let out the water with an excited whoosh.

Then Pete sucked in an even bigger gulp of water. His body puffed up to three times its normal size!

Grandfather Sea Turtle chuckled as he looked at Pete's spines. "Any big fish that thinks you will be a tasty little snack will be in for a big surprise."

From that day forward, Pete had many more adventures with his friends on the reef, but he never forgot the day that he learned how to be Pete the Pufferfish.

Describe how Pete protects himself.

Fluency

Miss Tam Goes Home

by Ann Watanabe
illustrated by Page Eastburn O'Rourke

"Life is an adventure," thought Miss Tam 7
as she settled into seat 17B and got ready for the 18
long airplane ride home. Just like her trips to 27
Ghana and Hawaii, Miss Tam's time in Australia 35
had gone by quickly. 39

It seemed like it was just yesterday that she 48
had retired from her job as a children's librarian 57
in Montgomery, Alabama. But here she was, 64
several months later, returning home from her 71
third grand adventure. 74

Fluency

Miss Tam pulled out her tattered journal. 7
She flipped through the pages and reviewed 14
her notes and photos. She recalled shopping 21
at Paddy's Market. "Great fruits, vegetables, 27
music, and people," she thought. "Bertha will 34
love my sheepskin boots! Oh, and I can't wait 43
to give Minnie Bird and Old Scraggly Cat 51
their gifts!" 53

Miss Tam flipped a page and read her 61
notes about the lemon rice pudding with 68
pears and vanilla ice cream. "Luscious, 74
delicious," thought Miss Tam. "I will have to 82
get the recipe." 85

Miss Tam smiled as she looked through page   8
after page of pictures and notes. When she got   17
to the pages about her dive at the Great Barrier   27
Reef, she grinned from ear to ear. She chuckled   36
as she looked at the underwater photos of   44
herself in pink fins, face mask, wetsuit, and   52
scuba gear. There she was, swimming among   59
parrotfish, clownfish, moray eels, and living   65
coral. Before she knew it, Miss Tam was in a   75
deep sleep.   77

Thirty hours later, Miss Tam was getting   84
out of a taxi in front of her home. She toddled   95
up the stairs, opened the door, and exclaimed,   103
"Hooly-dooly!"   105

"Hooly-dooly!" screeched Minnie Bird.   110

Glossary

advisor

A person who gives advice is called an **advisor**.

At school, if you need an *advisor*, you can talk to a teacher, a counselor, or the principal.

algae

Algae are living things that are usually found in water. Some kinds of algae are too small to see, and others grow very large.

Seaweed that washes up on the beach is one kind of *algae*.

approximately

If you do not know the exact number of something, but you can make a good guess, you say "**approximately**."

"About" and "around" often mean *approximately*.

Australia

Australia is one of Earth's seven continents. The continent has one country, and the country is also called Australia.

For our vacation, we sailed south to *Australia*.

colony

A **colony** is a group of animals that lives together.

Coral polyps live in *colonies*.

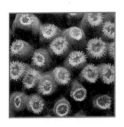

confused

When you don't understand something, you are **confused**.

The road signs didn't match the map, and Mr. Chapman was *confused* about which way to go.

continent

A **continent** is one of seven large land areas on Earth.

The United States is on the *continent* of North America.

contortion

When something is twisted out of its usual shape, it is called a **contortion**.

The magician went through many *contortions* to squeeze himself into a tiny box.

Glossary

coral polyp

A **coral polyp** is a sea animal with a tube-shaped body. Most are very small. Millions of coral polyps live together to form a coral reef.

Coral polyps live together to form coral reefs, and coral reefs are found in the ocean.

coral reef

A **coral reef** is an underwater habitat built by small animals called coral polyps.

John swam underwater and saw a *coral reef.*

disguise

Something that hides or changes the way you look is called a **disguise**.

Pam wanted to wear a *disguise*, so she put on a fake nose and glasses.

ecosystem

An **ecosystem** is a community of animals and plants living together in one area.

A coral reef and the fish that live around it are part of an *ecosystem.*

frustrated

If you are **frustrated**, you are upset and discouraged.

Isaac got *frustrated* when his bike tire went flat.

inflatable

Something **inflatable** can be filled with air or water.

We pumped up our *inflatable* raft and floated down the river.

leisurely

When you do something in a **leisurely** way, you take your time.

Aunt Sue took a *leisurely* walk through the garden.

nudibranch

A **nudibranch** is an animal that lives in the ocean. It has a soft body and is also called a sea slug.

Marisa had to write a report about *nudibranchs*.

Glossary

regulator

When you scuba dive, you put a **regulator** in your mouth to breathe. It is connected to an air tank.

Before John jumped off the boat to go diving, he put a tank on his back and a *regulator* in his mouth.

review

Review means to go back over something you've already looked at or studied.

Katrice *reviewed* her spelling words before the test.

4093 Specialty Place • Longmont, CO 80504 • 303-651-2829
www.sopriswest.com

READ·WELL

The Reef

Level 2

Sopris West®
EDUCATIONAL SERVICES

A Cambium Learning Company

ISBN-13: 978-1-60218-557-
ISBN-10: 1-60218-557-

167311

9 781602 185579